Interesting Stories from
Panchatantra

Author

VISHNU SHARMA

Compiled by

'KUNWAR' ANIL KUMAR

MANOJ PUBLICATIONS

CONTENTS

Manoj Publications

761, Main Road Burari, Delhi-110084
Phone : 27611116, 27611349
Fax : 27611546, Mobile : 9868112194
E-mail : manojpublications @vsnl.net
Website : www.manojpublications.com
ISBN : 81-8133-402-7

Showroom :

1583-84, Dariba Kalan,
Chandani Chowk, Delhi-6
Phone : 23262174, 23268216
Mobile : 9818753569

Printers :
Jain Offset Printers

THERE lived a Brahmin and his wife in a small village. The Brahmin couple had no children. They prayed day and night to God in order to be blessed with a child.

After years of praying, their wishes materialised and they were blessed with a child. But to everybody's shock, the child was a snake and not a normal human baby. The Brahmin couple was advised to get rid of the snake, as quickly as possible. But the Brahmin's wife didn't listen to their suggestions and continued to look after the snake as her own baby.

Years passed by and the snake grew up bigger and bigger, till he reached the age of marriage. Now the Brahmin couple started looking for a suitable girl for their snake son.

The Brahmin went from village to village and town to town in search of a suitable girl, but all in vain. "How can a human being marry our snake child?" said the Brahmin to his wife. But his wife insisted for a suitable match for her son.

Having lost all the hopes from all sides, the Brahmin approached one of his old friends. He narrated his problem to his friend. "Oh! you should've told me about it earlier," said his friend. "I'm myself looking for a suitable match for my daughter. I shall be too happy to give her in marriage with your snake son."

The Brahmin couldn't believe his ears. But the marriage was solemnized despite protests. The girl was herself adamant to marry Brahmin's son, be it a snake, no matter.

After marriage the newly married couple—the girl and the snake—started to live like an ideal wife and husband. The girl looked after her husband's comforts dutifully. Her husband—the snake—slept beside his wife coiled in a basket.

One night, the snake crawled out into a room. After a few moments a young man came out of the room. He woke up the girl. The girl seeing a man in his room was about to scream when the young man said to her, "Don't be foolish. I'm your husband."

The girl didn't believe the young man. She said, "Show it to me

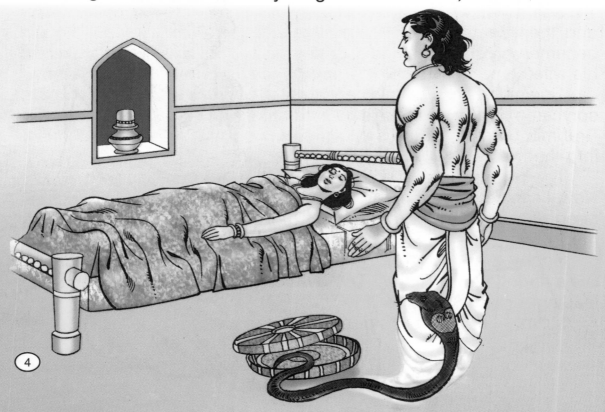

before my eyes. I still don't believe it."

So the young man again slipped into the empty shell of the snake and then came out of it again transformed into a man. The girl became very happy to find such a husband. When the Brahmin and his wife came to know of this secret, they too became very happy.

One night, the Brahmin kept a watch over his son. As soon as his son came out of the snake's body transformed into a young man, the Brahmin got hold of the snake's empty outer covering and threw it into the fire.

Then his son came to him and said, "Father, you've saved my life. Now, I can never be transformed into a snake. My outer covering has been destroyed in fire and with it has ended the long curse upon me."

So the Brahmin, his wife, son and daughter-in-law, all began to live a happy life, thereafter. The villagers too were happy to see them leading a normal and healthy life.

Moral—*After rains comes the sunshine.*

❑❑

THE DONKEY AND THE CUNNING FOX

ONCE there lived a foolish donkey in a town. The town was situated near a forest. There, in the forest lived king lion and his minister, a cunning fox. Once, king lion was badly wounded in a fierce fighting with an elephant. He became unable to hunt for his prey. So he asked his minister, the cunning fox to bring some good meal for him. As the fox used to share the prey, which king lion hunted for his meals, he at once, set out to search for food.

While wandering here and there, the fox met a donkey. The donkey looked foolish, nervous and hungry. The fox asked him, "Hello! you seem to be new to this forest. Where do you actually come from?"

"I come from the nearby town", said the donkey. "My master, the dhobi makes me work all day, but doesn't feed me properly. So I've left my home to find a better place to live in and eat properly."

"I see", said the fox. "Don't worry. I'm a senior minister in this forest kingdom. Come with me to the king's palace. Our king needs a bodyguard, who has the experience of town life. You will live in the palace and eat a lot of green grass growing around it."

The donkey was very happy to listen to all this from the minister fox of the forest kingdom. He proceeded with him to the royal palace.

Seeing a donkey before him the king lion became highly impatient and pounced upon him immediately. But on account of constant hunger, the king lion had gone weak. He couldn't overpower. The donkey freed himself and ran for his life.

"Your Majesty," said the fox to king lion, "you shouldn't have acted in such a haste. You have scared your prey."

"I'm sorry," said king lion. "Try to bring him here once again."

The hungry fox went again to the donkey and said to him, "What a funny fellow you are. Why did you run away like that?"

"Why shouldn't I?" asked the donkey.

"My dear," said the fox, "you were being tested for your alertness as a royal bodyguard of the king. Thank god, you showed a quick reflex, otherwise, you would have been rejected for the job."

The donkey believed what the fox said and accompanied him once again to the palace. There at the palace the king lion was hiding behind the thick bushes. As soon as the donkey passed by the bushes, the lion pounced upon him and killed him instantly.

Just when the lion was about to begin eating the donkey, the fox said, "Your Majesty, you're going to have your meals after quite a few days. It's better you first take a bath and offer prayers."

"Hmm!" the king lion roared and said to the fox, "Stay here. I'll be back right now."

The lion went to take bath and offer his prayers. In the meantime, the fox ate the donkey's brain. When the king lion came back to eat his prey, he was surprised to see that the donkey's brain was missing.

"Where is this donkey's brain?" The lion roared in anger.

"The donkey's brain!" the fox expressed his surprise. "Your Majesty, you're fully aware that donkeys don't have a brain. Had that donkey ever had a brain, he would never have come with me to this palace for the second time."

"Yes," agreed king lion, "that's the point." And he started eating happily the rest of the flesh of the dead donkey.

Moral—*Sometimes a cunning argument outwits normal intelligence.*

A POOR BRAHMIN'S DREAM

ONCE upon a time, there lived a poor Brahmin in a village. His name was Swabhavakripna. He was all alone in this world. He had no relatives or friends. He used to beg for his living. Whatever food he got as alms, he kept in an earthen pot and hung it beside his bed. Whenever he felt hungry he took out some food from the pot and ate it.

One night, the Brahmin lay on his bed and soon he was fast asleep. He began to dream—He was no longer a poor Brahmin. He wore good clothes. He was the owner of a shop. Hundreds of customers came to his shop. Soon he became richer than before. He purchased many buffaloes and cows. Very soon the buffaloes and cows had their young ones. Those young ones grew and became buffaloes and cows.

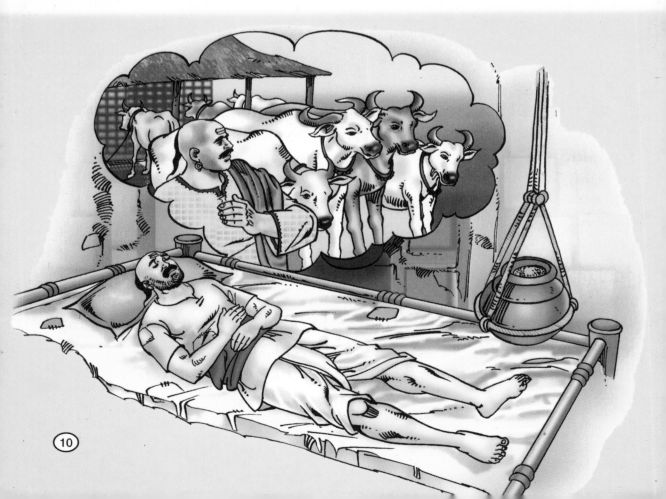

The buffaloes and cows gave milk. He made a lot of butter and curd from the milk. He sold butter and curd in the market. Soon he became richer then ever before. He built a big house for himself. Then he married a beautiful girl. Soon they had their children. The children played around all day making noise. He then scolded them and asked them to keep quiet. But they won't listen. So he picked up a stick and ran after them.

The Brahmin began to move his legs rapidly while he was still asleep. In doing so, he hit the earthen pot with one of his legs which was full of food. The pot broke and the food contents were spilled all over the floor. The Brahmin woke up. He saw that he was still in the bed. All the edible items kept in the pot were scattered on the ground and became unfit for eating. All this happened because of his day dreaming.

Moral—*One should not build castles in the air.*

❑❑

THE CAMEL WITH A BELL ROUND HIS NECK

THERE lived a cart-maker whose name was Ujjwalaka. He was not doing well in his business. Day by day, he was becoming poorer. Seeing no way out, the cart-maker decided to settle in some other town and try his luck there.

While the cart-maker and his family were travelling through a jungle, they saw a female camel suffering from labour pains. Seeing the female camel whining in pain, the cart-maker's wife pleaded with him to detain their journey for some time so that the poor animal could be rendered some help at this vital hour. The cart-maker's family stopped there and his wife began nursing the female camel. Soon, she gave birth to a baby camel. The cart-maker and his wife took great care and brought her to his house along with her baby. Gradually the baby camel grew to full size.

Fondly, the cart-maker tied a bell round the neck of the young camel. Now whenever, the young camel would move around, the bell would jingle.

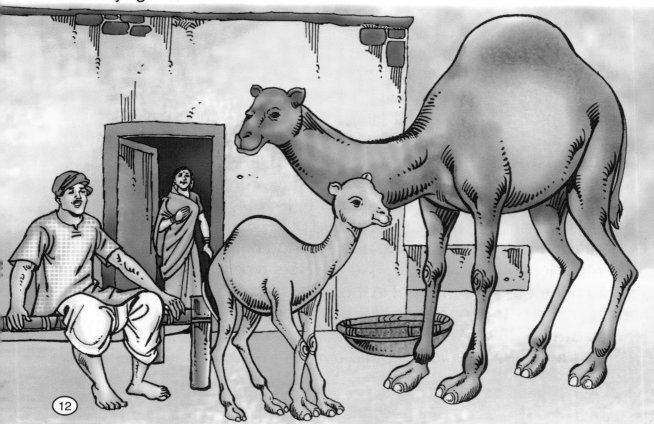

The cart-maker would sell the milk of the female camel and earn a lot of money. Soon he purchased one more female camel. The fortune smiled on the cart-maker and soon he became the owner of a number of camels.

All the camels used to go together to graze in a nearby jungle.

The young camel was in a habit of trailing behind other camels. This was of great concern to other camels. They advised the young camel not to stray behind. But the young camel didn't pay heed to their advice.

One day, the camels were grazing in a nearby jungle. A lion heard the jingling of the bells. He followed the sound and saw a caravan of young camels grazing. He noticed one camel with a bell round his neck, strayed behind and still eating grass. The other camels assuaged their hunger and went back home. The young camel began to loiter around. The lion in the meantime, hid himself behind a bush. When the camel came grazing near the bush the lion pounced upon him; killed and ate him.

Moral—*Take heed of a good advice.*

ONCE upon a time, there lived a Sanyasi in a Matha. His name was Dev Sharma. He was a learned man. Many people used to visit him for his valuable preachings and advices on important matters. They presented valuables and money to Dev Sharma. After sometime, Dev Sharma became very rich. The wealth he had amassed, became a great source of worry for him. He had to guard his wealth with great care. He always kept the money-bag under his armpit and never parted with it.

Once a thief whose name was Ashadhbhuti, came to know of Sanyasi's wealth. He made a plan to steal it. And in order to materialise his plan Ashadhbhuti approached Dev Sharma and expressed his desire to become his disciple.

"Om Namaha Shivaya", said Ashadhbhuti. "Gurudev, I'm tired of this worldly pleasure. Please accept me as one of your disciples and teach me the way to attain 'Moksha'."

"My child", said the Sanyasi, "I'm pleased with your words." The Sanyasi then performed some rituals to make Ashadhbhuti his disciple.

Now Ashadhbhuti messaged his Guru's hands and feet and waited upon him to wangle his affection and favour. But the Sanyasi didn't seem to fully trust Ashadhbhuti, because he never allowed him to enter the Matha at night. He also never parted with his money-bag. This was disappointing for Ashadhbhuti. But he didn't give up.

One day, the Sanyasi was invited to a nearby village to perform ceremony of sacred thread at one of his disciple's house.

The Sanyasi took the thief along with him. On the way, they came across a river. There Sanyasi folded his money-bag in his robe and said to his disciple, "Ashadhbhuti, look after this bag very carefully while I take my bath in the river."

After sometime, the Sanyasi returned having finished his holy bath. But Ashadhbhuti was not to be found there. Only his robe was lying on the ground. He quickly checked for the money-bag, but there was no money-bag in the robe. He began to cry, "I've been robbed". He swooned and fell on to the ground.

When he regained his conciousness, he became very sad and returned to his Matha—an unhappy and dejected man.

Moral—*Wealth may sometimes prove a source of all troubles.*

KING NANDA AND VARARUCHI

ONCE upon a time, there lived a king, by the name of Nanda. He was very brave. His fame spread far and wide. Many kings of the neighbouring kingdom bowed before him.

The king had a minister called Vararuchi. He was an expert in politics and a scholar of Sanskrit.

Once Vararuchi's wife became very angry with her husband. As Vararuchi loved his wife very much, he said to her, "Darling, what is it that makes you so angry? I'm ready do anything to make you happy."

"Then get your head shaved and fall at my feet, if you really wish to make me happy," said his wife flippantly.

Vararuchi did exactly as desired by his wife. His wife became happy and normalcy was restored in their life.

One day, king Nanda's wife also became angry with her husband. She refused to talk to the king. King Nanda also loved his wife very much. "Darling!" he said to his queen, "Tell me what is it that I can do to make you happy?"

"Well," replied the queen, "I'll put reins on your mouth, ride you like a horse. You must also neigh."

The king did exactly as desired by the queen. The queen also became happy and things became normal.

The next day, the king was sitting in his court. His minister Vararuchi came to him. The king looked at Vararuchi and laughed at him, "Vararuchi! why've you shaved your head all of a sudden? What's the reason?"

Vararuchi replied, "Your Majesty, I've shaved off my head for the same reason for which you neighed like a horse yesterday."

The king simply simpered. He could not utter a word.

TWO FISH AND A FROG

LONG, long ago, there lived two fish and a frog in a pond. The names of the two fish were Shatabuddhi and Sahasrabuddhi. The name of the frog was Ekabuddhi.

One day, when the three friends were talking to each other on the edge of the pond, some fishermen passed by. They were carrying baskets and nets with them. They saw the pond and said to one another, "This pond seems to be full of fish. Let's come tomorrow and catch them."

When the fishermen left the place, the frog said to the fish, "Friends, you also heard what the fishermen said. Let's leave this pond immediately and go to some other pond to save our lives."

But the two fish laughed. Sahasrabuddhi said, "Well, as far as I think the fishermen will never come back to catch us. But even if they do, they'll never be able to trap us, because we're expert swimmers and we know how to save ourselves."

But the frog was not convinced with the views of the fish. He said, "But I find myself not so expert in swimming. I'll definitely leave this

pond along with my family by this evening, to settle down in some other pond or well."

The same evening, the frog abandoned the pond along with his family and went to a nearby pond. The next day, the fishermen came to the pond. They cast their nets and caught all the fishes. The two fish tried to escape, but in vain. They also got trapped in the net and died.

When the frog and his wife saw the fishermen returning with a lot of fish in their net, they became very sad. They looked at the net with tearful eyes as they saw that their two friends.

Moral—*One should not turn a deaf ear to a friend's advice.*

WHY THE OWLS BECAME ENEMIES OF THE CROWS

Long, long ago, all the birds of a jungle gathered to choose a new bird as their king. They were not happy with their king the Garuda, who they thought always enjoyed his time in the heaven and never cared for the birds. So, they thought it was better to choose a new bird as their king.

A heated discussion followed in the meeting and ultimately it was decided to make the owl the king of birds. The birds started making preparation for the coronation of the newly elected king.

Just then a crow flew in and raised an objection in the meeting. He said laughing, "What a bird you've chosen as your king. An ugly fellow. He also goes blind during the day. Moreover, owls are birds of prey. He might kill other birds for his meals rather than save them. Didn't peacocks and swans suit as your king?"

The crow's arguments made the birds think over their decision again. It was decided to choose the king on some other occasion and hence the coronation ceremony was postponed.

The owl chosen as the king of birds, still waited for his coronation as king. He realised all of a sudden that there was absolute quiet around him. No one was talking, nothing was happening. Since, it was day time, he couldn't see anything around him. He grew very impatient and a little suspicious also. At last, overcome by his curiosity and eagerness for his coronation as king, he enquired from one of his attendants, the reason behind the delay.

"Sir," his attendant said, "The coronation ceremony has been postponed. All the birds have decided to chose a new king. Now not even a single bird is here. They have all gone back to their respective places.

"Why?" the owl asked angrily.

"A crow put up arguments against us,–the owl family. He said we're ugly and killers."

The 'would be' king owl further lost his temper and said to the smiling crow who was still present there, "You've deprived me of the honour of becoming a king. So, from now on, we are sworn enemies of each other. Beware of us."

The crow realised his folly, but it was too late now.

Moral—*Think twice before you do or say anything.*

THE DONKEY WHO SANG A SONG

ONCE upon a time, there lived a washerman in a village. He had a donkey by the name of Udhata. He used to carry loads of clothes to the river bank and back home everyday.

The donkey was not satisfied with the food, that was given to him by his master to eat. So he wandered into the nearby fields stealthily and ate the crops growing there.

Once, the donkey, while wandering around, happened to meet a fox. Soon, both of them became friends and began to wander together in search of delicious food.

One night, the donkey and the fox were eating water-melons in a field. The water-melons were so tasty, that the donkey ate in a large quantity. Having eaten to his appetite, the donkey became so happy that he was compelled by an intense desire to sing. He told the fox

that he was in such a good mood that he had to express his happiness in a melodious tone. "Don't be a fool. If you sing, the people sleeping in and around this field will wake up and beat us black and blue with sticks," said the fox worriedly.

"You are a dull fellow", the donkey said hearing the words of fox. "Singing makes one happy and healthy. No matter what comes, I'll definitely sing a song."

The fox became worried to see the donkey adamant to sing a song in the midst of the field, while the owner was still sleeping only a little distance away.

Seeing his adamance, he said to the donkey, "Friend, wait a minute before you start. First, let me jump over to the other side of the fence for my safety."

Saying so the fox jumped over to the other side of the fence without losing a moment.

The donkey began in his so-called melodious tone. Hearing, suddenly, a donkey braying in the field, the owner woke up from his sleep. He picked up his stick lying by his side and ran towards the donkey who was still braying happily. The owner of the field looked around and saw the loss caused by the donkey. He became very angry and beat him so ruthlessly that the donkey was physically incapacitated temporarily. He, somehow, managed to drag himself out of the field with great difficulty.

The fox looked at the donkey and said in a sympathetic tone, "I'm sorry to see you in this pitiable condition. I had already warned you, but you didn't listen to my advice."

The donkey too realised his folly and hung his head in shame.

Moral—_Think before you act._

THE RABBITS AND THE ELEPHANTS

ONCE upon a time, there lived a herd of elephants in a deep jungle. Their king was a huge elephant by the name of Chaturdanta. In the middle of this jungle, there was a big lake where all the animals went to drink water. Once it so happened, that it didn't rain for the whole year and the lakes went dry. The elephants, after a great deal of discussion, decided to move to the other forest, where there was a lake named Chandrasar. This lake was full of water and never went dry even if there were no rains.

And so, the elephants set out for the lake 'Chandrasar'. They felt very happy upon reaching the new lake. They bathed in the fresh water of the lake and also enjoyed playing and spewing water on each other by their trunks. After having bathed satisfactorily and quenched their thirst with the sweet water of the lake they came out of it and entered the deep forest.

But, there lived many rabbits in their burrows around the lake area. When the herd of elephants walked around they stamped the

burrows with their heavy feet. Thus, many rabbits were either killed or were left physically handicapped.

So, in order to salvage the grave situation, the rabbits held a meeting and discussed this new calamity. At one point, they decided to shift from that dangerous place and live somewhere else. But a rabbit named Lambkarna advised them to exercise patience. He offered his services for the sake of all the other rabbits and said, "Don't worry friends. Just see, how I drive these elephants away from this forest."

The next day, Lambkarna sat on a high rock. The rock lay in the main path of the elephants, leading to the lake. When the elephants passed by the rock, the rabbit addressed the king of the elephants in a tough voice, "You're a cruel fellow. You've trampled many of my relatives and friends under your feet. I too am king of rabbits. I stay in the heaven with God Moon. God Moon is very much annoyed with you."

The king elephant was frightened to hear this. He said in a trembling voice, "Please take me to God Moon. I'll ask for his forgiveness."

"All right", said the clever rabbit. "See me tonight at the lake."

The king elephant, then, as told by the rabbit, reached the lake at night. The king rabbit and the king elephant both stood near the edge of the lake. It was a silent and moonlit night. Mild breeze was blowing. The rabbit asked the elephant to look carefully into the water of the lake.

As soon as the king elephant looked into the lake, he saw the reflection of half moon in the lake's water. Just then a mild breeze blew and the reflection of the moon in the water became wavy.

Pointing to the wavy reflection of the moon, the king rabbit said, "Look for yourself, how annoyed God Moon is. Better you ask for his mercy, otherwise, he might curse you to death."

The king elephant became more and more frightened. He promised God Moon not to ever visit the lake with his friends.

The rabbits lived happily, thereafter.

LONG, long ago, there lived a weaver in a town by the name of Somilaka. The cloth he wove was so fine and beautiful that even the king liked it. But, somehow, he still remained a poor man, while other weavers were quite rich, even though they wove inferior cloth. This bitter fact made Somilaka sad. He left his native village and went to settle down in some other town to try his luck . In this town also, Somilaka couldn't earn much money. He became frustrated and decided to commit suicide. He made a rope of grass, prepared a noose and tied the rope's other end to the high branch of a tree. He put the noose round his neck. As he was about to jump on to the ground, he heard a voice from the heaven calling, "Hold it, don't commit suicide. It is I, God. I'm pleased with your hard work. Ask any boon of me and I'll grant it."

"Please give me a lot of wealth," said Somilaka. He was astonished to see God before him.

"But, what will you do with a lot of wealth?" asked God. "You don't need a lot of wealth, no more than what is required for your food and clothing."

"But I want a lot of wealth even then," replied Somilaka. "A man with money is respected everywhere, whether he spends it or not."

Seeing that Somilaka was adamant on his demand, God said, "First go to your native town and meet the two traders living there. One is known as 'Secret Wealth' and the other as 'Useful Wealth'."

Somilaka became very happy. He went back to his native town. There he decided to first observe the 'Secret wealth's living.

When 'Secret Wealth' saw Somilaka, he became very angry. He talked to Somilaka in an abusive language. 'Secret Wealth's wife offered him food in a broken plate. She also banged the glass of water on the floor. Somilaka didn't utter a word. He ate his food and thanked the family members of 'Secret Wealth' and left quietly. Then he went to meet 'Useful Wealth' trader.

'Useful Wealth' was much delighted to see Somilaka. Even the other members of his house welcomed him. They served him with delicious food. They talked to him in a friendly tone. At night, proper arrangements were made for him to take rest.

Early next morning, the king's servants arrived and brought money for 'Useful Wealth.'

When Somilaka observed this, he thought to himself: "This 'Useful Wealth' is not a wealthy man, but even then he lives more comfortably than the 'Secret Wealth'."

His wish for a lot of money was granted by God. He began to enjoy his wealth to the full, just like 'Useful Wealth.'

Moral—*Wealth must be used properly. Where necessary it must also be donated.*

❑❑

THERE stood a huge banyan tree on the outskirts of a small town. Thousands of crows lived in this tree. Not far from the banyan tree, there was a mountain cave. Thousands of owls lived in it.

The king of the owls accompanied by his soldiers used to hunt crows during the night. Soon thousands of crows were killed and eaten up by the owls. One of the main reasons for the killing of the crows at such a large scale was, that they were unable to see clearly during the night. And the owls, being nocturnal, could easily locate the crows sitting in the tree during night hours. And the unfortunate crows were defenceless; they couldn't fly away for the safety of their lives.

This kind of situation went on to such an extent, and the loss of lives of thousands of crows became so unbearable for the king of

crows that one day he was compelled to call a meeting to discuss ways and means to combat the situation and bring an end to the continuing disaster.

After heated discussions and exchange of views and ideas, a plan was chalked out in the meeting, according to which a drama was to be enacted at a little distance from the owls' cave.

So, on the next day, the drama was staged and while enacting the drama, an old crow was 'thrashed' and 'beaten mercilessly' by the king of crows and his soldiers. The seemingly half dead old crow, with a goat's blood sprinkled all over his body was later picked up by the soldiers of the king owl. This was done on the advice of a senior minister in king owl's cabinet. This minister had told the king owl. "Your Majesty, this badly wounded crow had spoken in favour of us in his king's cabinet meeting, saying that ours was a more intelligent and superior race, better managed and strong, hence we deserved the right to be known and recognized as the king of birds. This led to the murderous attack on the poor fellow."

"We should help him recuperate from his wounds and injuries,"

said the king of owls. "After this, we'll utilise this old knowledgeable crow's talent in demolishing their kingdom."

The old crow soon found a favourable place in the owls kingdom. Many of the owl ministers were in his favour, except, one or two, who opposed the crow, saying that he was, after all, from the enemy's camp.

Despite this opposition from certain owl ministers, the crow continued to live in the owls' cave.

Lastly, it was the day time when the owls themselves were not able to see anything, due to sunlight, when the seemingly wounded and infirm crow piled up thousands of wooden logs at the mouth of the owls' cave and put fire into it. The devouring flames leapt up high and all the owls in the owls' kingdom, inside the cave, were burnt to ashes.

Moral—_Never trust your enemy. Don't allow him into your home._

❑ ❑

ONCE upon a time, there lived a sparrow on a tree. He was very happy to have a beautiful and comfortable nest of his own. The sparrow used to fly to far off places to pick at grains from so many fields, full of crops. At the sun set he would return to his perch.

One day, the sparrow ate his fill, but could not return to his nest, because of the heavy rains which continued for the whole night. The sparrow had to spend the whole night in a big banyan tree a little distance away from home.

The next morning, when the rain stopped and the sky became clear, the sparrow returned to his tree. He was astonished to find a rabbit occupying his beautiful and comfortable nest.

The sparrow lost his temper and spoke to the rabbit, "It's my home you're sitting in. Please quit this place at once."

"Don't talk like fools," replied the rabbit. "Trees, rivers and lakes don't belong to anyone. Places like these are yours only so long as you are living in. If someone else occupies it in your absence, it belongs to the new occupant. So go away and don't disturb me anymore."

But the sparrow was not satisfied with this illogical reply. He said, "Let's ask a person of wisdom, then our case will be settled.

At a distance from the tree, there lived a wild cat. The cat, somehow, overheard the discussion that took place between the sparrow and the rabbit.

The cat immediately thought of a plan, took a holy dip in the river, and then sat like a priest and began chanting god's name in a loud tone. When the rabbit and the sparrow heard the chanting, they approached him with a hope to get impartial justice and requested him to pass a judgement in the matter.

The cat became very happy to have both of them in front of him. He pretended to listen to their arguments. But as soon as the right opportunity came, the cat pounced upon both of them and killed and ate them together with great relish.

Moral—*Tussle over triffle matters may sometimes lead to a certain disaster.*

THE MERCHANT AND THE BARBER

ONCE upon a time, there lived a merchant called by the name of Manibhadra, in a town known as Patliputra. He was of a charitable nature. But, somehow, due to misfortune, he lost all his wealth and became a pauper. His status in the society gradually came down. He became sad and dejected.

One night, as he lay in his bed, he started cursing his fate and thought of committing suicide by starving himself to death.

While thinking thus, he fell asleep. A Jain monk appeared in his dream and said to him, "Don't worry! I'm wealth, gathered by your forefathers. You are their legitimate heir. It's your legal right to possess me. Tomorrow, I shall come to your house in the guise of a jain monk. Just hit me on my head with a stick and I'll turn into solid gold."

The next morning, when the merchant woke up he felt pain in his head. He didn't believe his dream. In the meantime, his wife had called in a barber to massage her feet. Soon after the arrival of the

barber, a jain monk came to the merchant's house. The merchant welcomed the monk. He offered him seat and a glass of water. Then he hit the monk's head with a stick. The monk fell down and turned into gold from head to toe.

The merchant picked up the gold and hid it in a basement.

The barber who was a witness to all this thought to himself: 'I'll also invite these magical monks to my home to dine with me. When they come, I'll hit them on their heads, to turn them in gold. Soon I'll be a wealthy man'.

Then the barber went to the head monk and invited him and other monks to his house to dine with him. But the head monk refused the invitation. He said, "We are no Brahmins, who're invited to the houses to eat. Everyday, we collect alms and accept food only from the first devotee of the day. We eat to live only and not live to eat."

The barber then waited outside the monastery. When the monks came out, he requested them to come to his house and conduct prayers. A few monks agreed to it and went to the barber's house.

As soon as the monks entered the house, the barber hit them on their heads with a heavy stick. A few monks died, whereas a few others were badly injured.

The news of the barber hitting the monks spread in the town like wild fire. The barber was arrested by the authorities and taken to the court of law.

The judges asked the barber, "Why did you do this?"

The barber then narrated the whole story. He said, "I did it because I saw the merchant doing it."

Then the merchant was ordered to appear before the court. The merchant narrated the whole story.

The judges then ordered, "Let this wicked barber be hanged till death." The barber was then hanged to death.

Moral—*A blind imitation is always dangerous.*